THE
LAURA INGALLS WILDER
SONGBOOK

THE LAURA INGALLS WILDER SONGBOOK

Favorite songs from the "Little House" books
compiled and edited by Eugenia Garson

Arranged for piano and guitar
by Herbert Haufrecht

Illustrated by Garth Williams

HARPER & ROW, PUBLISHERS
NEW YORK, EVANSTON, AND LONDON

THE LAURA INGALLS WILDER SONGBOOK

LIBRARY OF CONGRESS CATALOG CARD NUMBER: 68-24327

Table of Contents

Preface

Laura Ingalls Wilder's memories were filled with the songs of her girlhood, and so it was natural that music should have played an important part in the "Little House" books, her warmly glowing, firsthand account of family life in pioneer days. From her earliest years when Laura, her parents, her elder sister Mary, and Baby Carrie lived in a log house on the edge of the Big Woods in Wisconsin, Pa sang and played his fiddle for them. When Pa and Ma—Charles and Caroline Ingalls—packed up the covered wagon that was to carry them all farther west, the fiddle in its box was laid carefully between pillows. Its tunes lulled Laura to sleep beside the family campfires all across the plains of Kansas and into Indian country.

After a year in a log cabin on the prairie, the wagon moved them again, this time to Minnesota. Living first in a sod house dug from the banks of Plum Creek, then in the new home Pa had built nearby, Laura and Mary went to school and church for the first time. It was during this year that Mary lost her sight as the result of scarlet fever.

Another long trip, now with a new baby sister, Grace, brought them to a railroad builders' camp in Dakota Territory, where Pa became a railroader for a time. When work stopped for the winter, the Ingalls family stayed on in the surveyors' house. Here they were isolated for months until the arrival of neighbors—Mr. and Mrs. Boast—brought them company and the enjoyment of song-filled evenings.

In the spring, Pa filed his claim for a homestead near the new townsite of De Smet, South Dakota, and put up the first building in town. Then came the grim experience of the snowbound winter when Almanzo Wilder, Laura's future husband, risked his life to bring wheat to the starving settlers. Later the family settled down to summers in a claim shanty on the prairie and sheltered winters in town. While Laura taught school and helped with Mary's expenses at a college for the blind, she was being courted by Almanzo. As the eighth book of the saga concludes, Laura and Almanzo marry and go to live in a little house of their own.

There had been music of many kinds along the way: the merry tunes at Grandpa's dance back in Wisconsin, Ma's gentle hymns during lonely prairie evenings, Cousin Lena's songs at Silver Lake, and the choruses at the singing class where Almanzo was Laura's escort. Church and Sunday school, revival meetings, and patriotic celebrations had their part, as did the "Literaries"—evening gatherings that took place when the little settlement of De Smet began to grow into a community. And in hard times or good there had always been Pa's songs and the voice of the fiddle, echoing longest of all.

The Little House in the Big Woods was published in 1932; as a children's librarian I welcomed it not only as a wonderful, true story but as a reminder of the basic values so greatly needed in that time of economic depression. As I shared each succeeding volume with the boys and girls in the library, there came repeated comments and questions about the songs that were so often mentioned in the text. Favorites were greeted with delighted recognition; others were tantalizing because they were so elusive. Surely they were as real as everything else in the books! Sometimes songs were available but difficult for young people to play; sometimes words and melodies could not be found, nor was information about them easy to locate. Finally I decided to make a thorough study of all the songs that played a part in the "Little House" series.

The undertaking proved to be lengthy, interesting, and unexpectedly complex. Reference works on folk, religious, and popular music were consulted. The many subdivisions in these fields made it necessary to go through scores of volumes in order to winnow a few items of information. Some songs had never been widely known; others had attained enormous popularity in their day, only to pass into obscurity and the files of music libraries and collections; a few were known by several titles. Authors and composers were not always correctly identified; hymns were sung to many different tunes; reprinting brought changes in words and melody; and folk songs had countless versions.

Early sheet music, hymnals, song albums, and broadsides were examined and compared. Line-by-line collation was necessary where neither title nor first line was known— indeed, many older books had no indexes at all. Eventually it was possible to trace almost all the songs, with verified related data, and a generous selection appears here.

Many of Mrs. Wilder's songs were handed down through oral tradition, and her texts sometimes differed from the originals. In almost every instance her wording and punctuation have been followed. In the case of a few of the longer songs some stanzas have been dropped. Whenever information about the song, composer, or lyricist was available, I have included a brief note above the music. This is followed by a few sentences indicating where each song appears in the "Little House" series. The title of the book and the number of the page on which the song first occurs is also given. Titles are abbreviated as follows:

LHBW	*Little House in the Big Woods*
LHP	*Little House on the Prairie*
FB	*Farmer Boy*
BPC	*On the Banks of Plum Creek*
SSL	*By the Shores of Silver Lake*
LW	*The Long Winter*
LTP	*Little Town on the Prairie*
HGY	*These Happy Golden Years*

The collection offers a fascinating cross section of songs that went westward with the pioneers. There are airs deeply rooted in the Scottish and English folk tradition, as well as some with a native homespun quality. A number of these tunes were used for dancing or as singing games to be sung and stepped to without music at "play parties" in areas where, for religious reasons, dancing was frowned upon. There are patriotic songs, sentimental ballads, and rhythmic minstrel-show and music-hall melodies. Old hymns are included together with the gospel songs of the nineteenth-century revivalists. The singing school, where people sang together the music they had taken pleasure in learning, is recalled, as are the "singing families" whose concert tours were so successful during the 1840's and 1850's.

The individuality of this widely varied material, ranging from intricate choral settings to single-staff manuscript notation, has been admirably expressed in Herbert

Haufrecht's completely new arrangements, which succeed in capturing the spirit of the originals while making them invitingly easy to play and sing.

Grateful acknowledgment of their helpful cooperation is made to the librarians in the Music and Copyright divisions of the Library of Congress, particularly to Mrs. Rae Korson of the Archive of Folk Song; the Music Departments of The Free Library of Philadelphia and The Buffalo and Erie County Public Library of Buffalo, New York; the Salvation Army Library and the Union Theological Seminary Library in New York City, with special thanks to the staffs of the American History and Music Reference Divisions of the New York Public Library, where most of the work was done; and to Mr. and Mrs. L. D. Lichty, Curators of the Laura Ingalls Wilder Home and Museum in Mansfield, Missouri. Appreciation is also due the late Sigmund Spaeth, author of *A History of Popular Music in America*, James J. Fuld, author of *The Book of World-Famous Music*, and the many other authorities on American music whose published works, too numerous to mention individually, are of incalculable value to the collector.

E. G.

Home and Memories

The Beacon-Light of Home

Words by George F. St. Clair   Music by H. M. Estabrooke   1879

After the Ingalls family had settled into their little claim shanty near De Smet, they rested outdoors in the beautiful spring evening. Darkness was falling softly on the prairie, and the stars came out one by one over the huge sky. Pa felt like music, and this is the song he played.   SSL, *page 265*

1. When the stars are bright-ly beam-ing, And the sigh - ing winds are still, When
far than gold or glo - ry Is that cot - tage thatched and old, Where

twi - light shad - ows hov - er o'er the lea, There's a
ros - es bud and blos - som round the door, For a

ti - ny can - dle gleam - ing From the cot - tage 'neath the hill, And I
wom - an dwells with - in it With a heart as pure as gold, And her

know that lit - tle bea - con shines for me. I can
love is all my own for - ev - er - more. When the

see its cheer - ful glim - mer From my boat down in the bay, When
wea - ry day is o - ver And the world has gone to rest, When my

for Chorus
repeat verse
to Fine

The Floating Scow of Old Virginia

Words and Music by Charles T. White   1847

Charles T. White was a celebrated Negro singer and composer.
Pa came into the shanty with an armful of wood and said: "This wind takes
your breath away. Soon as I can thaw out my fingers, we'll have a tune to
drown the yowl of that wind." But when Ma heard the music, she cried: "For
pity's sakes! I'd as soon listen to the wind."   LW, *page 42*

1. The float - ing scow of old __ Vir - gin - ia I worked from day __ to day, __ A -
2. Oh, if __ I were young __ a - gain, I'd lead __ a dif - ferent life, __ Lay
3. Oh, when __ I'm dead and gone __ to rest, Lay the old ban - jo by __ my side, __ Let the

rak-ing a-mong the oys-ter beds, To me it was but
up some mon-ey and buy some land, And take Di-nah for my
'pos-sum and 'coon to the fu-ner-al go For they were my on-ly

play. But now I'm old and fee-ble too, I
wife. But now I'm get-ting old and gray, I
pride. Then in soft re-pose I'll take my sleep, And

can-not work an-y more. Oh, car-ry me back to
can-not work an-y more. Oh, car-ry me back to
I'll dream for-ev-er-more. You car-ried me back to

old Vir - gin - ia, To the old __ Vir - gin - ia shore. ____
old Vir - gin - ia, To the old __ Vir - gin - ia shore. ____
old Vir - gin - ia, To the old __ Vir - gin - ia shore. ____

Chorus

Oh, car - ry me back to old Vir - gin - ia, To old Vir - gin - ia shore, Oh, __

car - ry me back to old Vir - gin - ia, To old __ Vir - gin - ia shore. ____

Ben Bolt

Words by Dr. Thomas Dunn English   Music by Nelson Kneass   1848

Dr. English never received payment for this immensely popular song, and the musical accompaniment he wrote for it has been forgotten. The present melody is based on an old German tune.

When Mr. and Mrs. Boast settled in at Silver Lake, their voices rounded out the family's evenings of song. This was a favorite selection. SSL, *page 213*

1. Oh, do you re-mem-ber sweet Al-ice, Ben Bolt, Sweet Al-ice, with eyes _ so brown, Who wept with de-light when you

2. Oh, do you re-mem-ber the wood,_ Ben Bolt, Near the green sun-ny slope of the hill, Where oft we have sung 'neath its

3. Oh, do you re-mem-ber the school,_ Ben Bolt, And the Mas-ter so kind and so true, And the lit-tle nook by the

gave her a smile, And trem-bled with fear — at your frown? In the
wide spread-ing shade, And kept time to the click — of the mill? The
clear run-ning brook, Where we gath-er'd the flow-'rs as they grew? On the

old church-yard in the val-ley, Ben Bolt, In a cor-ner ob-scure and a-
mill has gone to de-cay, — Ben Bolt, And a qui-et now reigns all a-
Mas-ter's grave grows the grass, Ben Bolt, And the run-ning lit-tle brook is now

lone, They have fit-ted a slab of __ gran-ite so gray, And sweet
round, See, the old rus-tic porch, with its ros-es so sweet, Lies __
dry, And of all __ the friends who were school-mates then, There re-

Al - ice lies un - der the stone;
scat-ter'd and fal-len to the ground;
mains, Ben, but you — and — I.

They have fit-ted a slab of —
See, the old rus - tic porch, with its
And of all — the friends who were

gran-ite so gray, And sweet Al - ice lies un - der the stone.
ros - es so sweet, Lies — scat-ter'd and fal - len to the ground.
school - mates then, There re - mains, Ben, but you — and — I.

Keep the Horseshoe over the Door

Words and Music by J. P. Skelly   1880

Skelly, a plumber by trade, also wrote popular songs of many types.
Over the door of the brand-new claim shanty Pa hung his rifle and a bright new
horseshoe. Later when he sang about the good luck this would bring, Ma said:
"It sounds rather heathenish to me, Charles." SSL, *page 284*

1. We journey along quite contented with life, And try to live peaceful with all; We keep ourselves free from all trouble and
2. The horseshoe is lucky, that's what they all say, It keeps out the spirit of wrong; It brings in the fairies at night and at
3. If you're starting in life with a sweet little wife, And want to be happy and gay, Just get an old horseshoe to hang on the

strife, And we're glad when our friends on us call. _____ Our
day, As a guard-ian 'tis sim - ple but strong; _____ When you
wall, And keep all the witch-es a - way; _____ Then

home it is hap - py and cheer - ful and bright, We're con - tent and we
come home at night it will keep you from fright, It brings to you
safe - ly you'll sail o - ver life's storm - y sea, And land on a

ask noth - ing more, _____ And the rea - son we pros - per I'll
bless - ings ga - lore; _____ Wher - e'er you may dwell you will
rose cov - er'd shore; _____ Though strange it may seem, ev - 'ry -

tell to you now, There's a horse-shoe hung o - ver the door. _____
al - ways do well, When the horse-shoe hangs o - ver the door. _____
where you will see The old horse-shoe hung o - ver the door. _____

Chorus

Keep the horse-shoe hung o - ver the door, _____ It will bring you good luck ev - er - more; _____ If you want to be hap - py and free from all care, Keep the horse-shoe hung o - ver the door. _____

Life Let Us Cherish

Words and Music by Hans Georg Nägeli   *1796*

Early sheet music attributes this to Mozart; however, it is actually the work of
Hans Georg Nägeli, a Swiss music educator and publisher.
When grasshoppers ate the crops so that Pa had to walk back East to get a job,
this was the last song he played before putting away the fiddle.   BPC, *page 211*

toil and care, Why choose the ran - kling thorn to wear, And
at - mos-phere, And fork - éd light - nings rend the air, The

D. C. al Fine

heed - less by the lil - y stray Which blos - soms in — the way. —
sun re - sumes his sil - ver crest, And smiles a - down the west. —

3. The genial seasons soon are o'er,
   Then let us ere we quit this shore
   Contentment seek; it is life's zest,
   The sunshine of the breast.

   (Chorus)

4. Away with every toil and care,
   And cease the rankling thorn to wear,
   With manful hearts life's conflict meet
   Till death sounds the retreat.

   (Chorus)

Oft in the Stilly Night

Words by Thomas Moore   Traditional Scottish Tune   1815

A pensive melody that appeared in Moore's *Selection of Popular National Airs*.
This song was one of Abraham Lincoln's favorites.

Toward the end of a lively musical evening, Pa would play some old tunes like
this one "to go to sleep on," he said.   SSL, *page 213*

1. Oft in the still - y night, Ere slum - ber's chain has bound ___ me, Sweet mem - 'ry brings the light Of oth - er days a - round me. The smiles, the tears, of

2. When I re - mem - ber all The friends so link'd to - geth - er, I've seen a - round me fall Like leaves in win - ter weath - er, I feel like one who

boy - hood's years, The words of love then spo - ken;
treads a - lone Some ban - quet hall de - sert - ed, Whose

eyes that shone, now dimmed and gone, The cheer - ful hearts now bro - ken.
lights are fled, whose gar - lands dead, And all but he de - part - ed.

Chorus

Thus in the still - y night, Ere slum - ber's chain hath bound ___ me,

Sad mem - 'ry brings the light Of oth - er days a - round me.

Rock Me to Sleep

Words by Elizabeth Akers Allen (pseud. Florence Percy)
Music by William Martin   1860

The "Literaries," evening get-togethers of the Literary Society, were started in De Smet to give everybody a good time. There was a different program every Friday, and anyone who could help pitched in. At the musical evening Laura could hardly bear the sadness of this song. All the women were wiping their eyes, and the men were clearing their throats.   LTP, *page 223*

1. Back - ward, turn back - ward, Oh Time in thy flight,
2. O - ver my heart____ in days that are flown,

Make me a child a - gain just for to - night.
No love like moth - er love ev - er was shown;

Moth - er, come back from the
No oth - er wor - ship a -

ech - o - less shore,
bides and en - dures,

Take me a - gain to your heart as of yore;
Faith - ful, un - self - ish, and pa - tient like yours;

Kiss from my fore - head the fur - rows of care,
None like a moth - er can charm a - way pain
Smooth the few silver threads out of my hair,
soul and the world - wea - ry brain.
O - ver my slum - bers your lov - ing watch keep;
Slum - ber's soft calm o'er my heav - y lids creep;
Rock me to sleep, moth-er, rock me to sleep!
Rock me to sleep, moth-er, rock me to sleep!

3. Mother, dear mother, the years have been long
   Since I last hushed to your lullaby song;
   Sing then and unto my soul it shall seem
   Womanhood's years have been only a dream.
   Clasped to your heart in a loving embrace,
   With your light lashes just sweeping my face,
   Never hereafter to wake or to weep;
   Rock me to sleep, mother, rock me to sleep!

Love's Old Sweet Song

Words by Clifton Bingham   Music by James L. Molloy   1884

James Lyman Molloy, an Irish lawyer, was also well-known as a composer. This is the most famous of his songs.

The evening before Laura's wedding Pa played all the old tunes that she had known ever since she could remember and finished with "Just a song at twilight...." HGY, *page 277*

Once in the dear dead days be-yond re-call   When on the world the
E - ven to-day we   hear love's song of yore,   Deep in our hearts it

mists be-gan to fall,   Out of the dreams that rose in hap-py throng,
swells for-ev-er-more.   Foot-steps may fal - ter, wea-ry grow the way,

Low to our hearts love sang an old sweet song.
Still we can hear it at the close of day.
And in the dusk where
So to the end when

fell the fire-light gleam
life's dim shad-ows fall,
Soft-ly it wove it-self in-to our dream.
Love will be found the sweet-est song of all.

Chorus

Just a song at twi-light, when the lights are low

And the flick-'ring shad-ows soft-ly come and

go, Though the heart be wea - ry, sad the day and
long, Still to us at twi - light comes love's old
song, Comes love's old sweet song.

Favorites of Long Ago

Buy a Broom

Words Anonymous   Traditional Austrian Tune   Circa 1830

This nursery favorite was originally popular with adults; an early presentation
at the Park Theatre in New York met with "the most Unbounded Approba-
tion." It was a song that Laura loved when she learned it from her Cousin Lena
in the railroad camp at Silver Lake.   SSL, *page 94*

wan-d'ring Ba - var - ian a broom? Buy a broom, buy a

broom! Will you buy of__ this__ wan-d'ring Ba - var - ian a broom?

2. To brush off the insects that come to annoy you
   You'll find it quite useful by night and by day,
   And what better exercise, pray can employ you,
   Than to sweep all vexatious intruders away?
   Buy a broom, buy a broom!
   Than to sweep all vexatious intruders away?

3. Ere winter comes on for sweet home soon departing
   My toils for your favor again I'll resume,
   And while gratitude's tear in my eyelid is starting,
   Bless the time that in England I cried buy a broom!
   Buy a broom, buy a broom!
   Bless the time that in England I cried buy a broom!

Camptown Races

Words and Music by Stephen Foster   1850

Many of Stephen Foster's melodies are reminiscent of Negro folk music; the
chorus of "Camptown Races" is similar to "Roll, Jordan, Roll."
The music would go rollicking while Pa and Mr. Boast sang: "I bet my money
on the bob-tailed mare!" Ma did not approve of gambling, but her toe could
not stop tapping to this tune.   SSL, *page 212*

go back home with a pock-et full of tin, Oh! doo-dah - day!
Can't touch bot-tom with a ten - foot pole, Oh! doo-dah - day!

Chorus

Goin' to run all night! Goin' to run all day! I

bet my mon-ey on the bob-tailed mare And you bet yours on the gray!

3. Old muley cow come onto the track,   Doo-dah! doo-dah!
   The bobtail fling her over her back,   Oh! doo-dah-day!
   Then fly along like a railroad car,   Doo-dah! doo-dah!
   Running a race with a shooting star,   Oh! doo-dah-day!

   (Chorus)

4. See them flying on a ten-mile heat,   Doo-dah! doo-dah!
   Round the racetrack, then repeat,   Oh! doo-dah-day!
   I win my money on the bobtailed mare,   Doo-dah! doo-dah!
   I keep my money in an old tow bag,   Oh! doo-dah-day!

   (Chorus)

Golden Years Are Passing By

Words and Music by Will L. Thompson   1879

Will L. Thompson was a prolific nineteenth-century song writer whose sentimental ballads enjoyed great popularity.

The family sat in the deepening dusk. The land flattened to blackness, and in the clear air above it the stars hung low. Then Pa said: "Here is one for you girls." Softly he sang; the music drifted away and was gone.   HGY, *page 156*

1. Gold - en years are pass - ing by,— Hap - py, hap - py gold-en years, Pass - ing on the wings of time, These hap - py gold - en years. Call them back as they go by, Sweet their mem - 'ries

2. Gold - en years are pass - ing by,— Pre - cious, pre - cious gold-en years, Let no i - dle hour be spent, With sor - row, grief, and tears. Ah! The good we all may do, As the mo - ments

are, ___ Oh, im - prove them as they fly, These hap - py gold - en years.
pass, ___ To your no - bler self be true, Re - ward will come at last.

Chorus

Gold - en years, gold - en years, Hap - py gold - en years, ___

Oh, im - prove them as they fly, These hap-py gold - en years.

3. Golden years are passing by,
Fleeting, fleeting swiftly on,
Life is but a passing hour,
Before we know 'tis gone;
Soon the parting time will come,
Day by day it nears.
Have you done your duty well,
These happy golden years?

(Chorus)

Paddle Your Own Canoe

Words and Music by Harry Clifton   1867

This is one of the moralizing songs, based on homely maxims, that were highly esteemed during the late nineteenth century.

Comfortably settled in at Silver Lake's deserted railroad camp forty miles away from the nearest neighbors, Pa said: "Now here's something worth singing. It's what we'll be doing this winter."   SSL, *page 148*

1. I've trav-eled a-bout   a   bit in   my   time, And of   trou-bles I've   seen   a
2. It's   all   ver-y well to de-pend on a   friend, That   is if you've proved   him

few; _____   But   found   it   bet-ter   in   ev - 'ry   clime   To
true, _____   But you'll   find   it   bet-ter   by   far   in   the   end   To

pad - dle my own ca - noe. _____ My wants are few, ___ I
pad - dle your own ca - noe. _____ To "bor-row" is dear-er by

care not at all If my debts are paid when due. _____ I
far than to "buy," ___ A max-im tho' old still true; _____ You

drive a - way strife in the o-cean of life While I pad-dle my own_ ca - noe._
nev-er will sigh if you on-ly will try___ To pad-dle your own_ ca - noe._

Chorus

Then love your neigh - bor as your - self, As the

world you go trav-el-ing through,_____ And nev-er sit down, with a

tear or a frown, But pad-dle your own ca-noe._____

3. If a hurricane rise in the midday skies,
   And the sun is lost to view;
   Move steadily by with a steadfast eye,
   And paddle your own canoe;
   The daisies that grow in the bright green fields
   Are blooming so sweet for you,
   So never sit down, with a tear or a frown,
   But paddle your own canoe.

   (Chorus)

It Will Never Do to Give It Up So

Words and Music by Daniel Decatur Emmett   1843

This was one of Daniel Emmett's early minstrel successes. The chorus shows the influence of Irish and Scottish reels.

During one of the long winter's savage blizzards when Pa's hands were too cracked and stiff to play the fiddle, he led the family in singing this spirited ditty about facing up to trouble on "the old Jim River."   LW, *page 291*

Lively, banjo style

1. I'm old Mis-ter Brown just from the South, I
2. The old Jim Riv-er I float-ed down, I

G

so, Mis-ter Brown, It will nev-er do to give it up so.

3. The old log rake me aft and fore,
It left my cookhouse on the shore;
I thought it wouldn't do to give it up so
So I scull myself ashore with the old banjo.

    (Chorus)

4. I gets on shore and feels very glad,
I looks at the banjo and feels very mad;
I walks up the bank that's slick as glass,
Up went my heels and I light upon the grass.

    (Chorus)

5. By golly, but it surely made me laugh,
With my boat I made a raft;
I had a pine tree for a sail
And steered her down with my coattail.

    (Chorus)

6. That same night as the sun did set,
I 'rived in town with my clothes all wet;
Then I built up a great big fire,
If that's not true then I am a liar.

    (Chorus)

Oh, Susanna

Words Traditional USA, California Gold Rush Version
Music by Stephen Foster   1848

This parody of Stephen Foster's minstrel ditty was called "The California Immigrant"; it was first heard at the farewell banquet for a young man who was leaving for California on the sailing ship *Eliza*. The new version became the theme song of the forty-niners and later pioneers.

Pa often sang it beside his prairie campfire.   LHP, *page 333*

Chorus

Oh Su-san-na, Don't you cry for me! I'm____ going to Cal - i - for - ni - a, With my wash-pan on my knee!

2. I jumped aboard the *'Liza* ship
   And traveled on the sea,
   And every time I thought of home,
   I wished it wasn't me!
   The vessel reared like any horse,
   That had of oats a wealth,
   I found it wouldn't throw me so
   I thought I'd throw myself!

   (Chorus)

3. I thought of all the pleasant times
   We've had together here,
   I thought I ought to cry a bit,
   But couldn't find a tear.
   The pilot's bread* was in my mouth,
   The gold dust in my eye,
   And though I'm going far away,
   Dear brothers, don't you cry!

   *(hard tack)

   (Chorus)

4. I soon shall be in Frisco
   And there I'll look around,
   And when I see the gold lumps there,
   I'll pick them off the ground.
   I'll scrape the mountains clean, my boys,
   I'll drain the rivers dry,
   A pocketful of rocks bring home,
   So brothers, don't you cry!

   (Chorus)

The Campbells Are Coming

Words and Music Traditional Scottish   Circa 1715

The evening before starting his three-hundred-mile walk to get work, Pa played for a long time in the twilight. This stirring march was one of the tunes. When bedtime came, he said: "Take good care of the old fiddle, Caroline. It puts heart into a man."   BPC, *page 211*

Verse

1. Up - on the Lo - monds I lay, I lay, ___ Up -
on the Lo - monds I lay, I lay; I look - ed down ___ to
bon - nie Loch Lev - en, And heard ___ the bon - nie pi - brochs play.

2. The great Ar - gyle, ___ he goes be - fore; ___ He
makes his can - nons loud - ly roar; Wi' sound o' trum - pet,
pipe, and drum, The Camp - bells are com - ing, Hur - rah! ___ Hur - rah!

D. C. al Fine

3. The Campbells they are a' in arms;
   Their loyal faith and truth to show;
   Wi' banners rattling in the wind,
   The Campbells are coming, Hurrah! Hurrah!

(Chorus)

49

All the Blue Bonnets Are over the Border

Words by Sir Walter Scott   Traditional Scottish Tune   Circa 1820

The "Border Ballad" from Scott's *Monastery*, set to an ancient Scottish air, became widely popular in the United States during the early nineteenth century. Its rousing strains helped to ease the rigors of the long winter. Pa said: "Blamed if that old tune don't give me the spunk to like fighting even a blizzard!" LW, *page 43*

March! March! Ett - rick and Tev - iot - dale!

Why, my lads, din - na ye march for - ward in or - der? March! March!

Esk - dale and Lid - des - dale! All the blue bon - nets are o - ver the bor - der!

Verse

1. Man - y   a   ban - ner spread,   flut - ters a - bove   your head,
2. Come from   the   hills where   your   hir - sels are   graz - ing,

simile

Man - y   a crest that is   fa - mous in   sto - ry: Mount, and make read - y   then,
Come from the glen   of the   buck and the   roe;____   Come to   the crag where the

D. C. al Fine

sons of the moun - tain glen,   Fight! for your homes and the   old Scot - tish glo - ry!
bea - con is   blaz - ing,   Come with the buck - ler, the   lance, and the bow.____

3. Trumpets are sounding, war steeds are bounding,
   Stand to your arms and march in good order;
   England shall many a day tell of the bloody fray,
   When the blue bonnets came over the border.

(Chorus)

Where There's a Will There's a Way

Words and Music by Harry Clifton   1867

The hard winter was over; the train had come at last with food. The Ingalls family and their friends the Boasts celebrated springtime by having the Christmas dinner they had all gone without. Afterwards everyone joined in this new song, and as they sang fear and suffering seemed to rise like a dark cloud and float away on the music.   LW, *page 334*

1. This life is a dif - fi - cult rid - dle For how man - y peo - ple we see ___ With
2. Did you nev - er hear tell of the spi - der That tried up the wall hard to climb? ___ If
3. Do you think that by sit - ting and sigh - ing You'll ev - er ob - tain all you want? ___ It's

Ballads, Games, and Dances

Billy Boy

Words and Music Traditional USA

This folk song is a nonsense version of the grim classic ballad "Lord Randal."
The happy winter evenings had begun at Silver Lake. Gaily, Pa played and
sang: "She can make a cherry pie, charming Billy." His eyes twinkled at Ma
while the music laughed and whirled.   SSL, *page 212*

Moderately, brightly

1. Oh,_____ where have you been, Bil - ly
2. Did she bid you to come in, Bil - ly

boy, Bil - ly boy; Oh,_____ where have you
boy, Bil - ly boy; Did she bid you to come

been, charm - ing Bil - ly?   I have been to seek a
in, charm - ing Bil - ly?   Yes, she bade me to come

wife; She's the joy___ of my life, But she's a
in; There's a dim-ple in her chin, But she's a

young thing and can - not leave her moth - er. ___
young thing and can - not leave her moth - er. ___

3. Did she set for you a chair, Billy boy, Billy boy;
   Did she set for you a chair, charming Billy?
   Yes, she set for me a chair;
   She has ringlets in her hair,
   But she's a young thing and cannot leave her mother.

4. Can she make a cherry pie, Billy boy, Billy boy;
   Can she make a cherry pie, charming Billy?
   She can make a cherry pie,
   With a twinkle in her eye,
   But she's a young thing and cannot leave her mother.

5. Is she often seen at church, Billy boy, Billy boy;
   Is she often seen at church, charming Billy?
   Yes, she's often seen at church,
   With a bonnet white as birch,
   But she's a young thing and cannot leave her mother.

6. How tall is she, Billy boy, Billy boy;
   How tall is she, charming Billy?
   She's as tall as any pine,
   And as straight as a pumpkin vine,
   But she's a young thing and cannot leave her mother.

7. Are her eyes very bright, Billy boy, Billy boy;
   Are her eyes very bright, charming Billy?
   Yes, her eyes are very bright,
   But, alas, they're minus sight,
   But she's a young thing and cannot leave her mother.

8. How old is she, Billy boy, Billy boy;
   How old is she, charming Billy?
   She is four times seven,
   Twenty-eight and eleven,
   But she's a young thing and cannot leave her mother.

57

Buffalo Gals

Words and Music by John Hodges (pseud. Cool White) 1848

Originally called "Lubly Fan," this minstrel-show number and play-party song underwent various changes of name to fit different localities. When the fiddle sang it at Grandpa's dance and Pa called "Swing your partners," skirts swirled and boots stamped and partners bowed and separated and met and bowed again.   LHBW, *page 145*

1. As   I   went   lum - b'ring   down   the   street,
2. I   ax'd   her   if   she'd   have   some   talk,
3. I'd   like   to   make   that   gal   my   wife,

Down   the   street,   down   the   street,   A   love - ly   gal   I
Have   some   talk,   have   some   talk,   Her   feet   cov-ered up   the
Gal   my   wife,   gal   my   wife,   I   would   be   hap - py

58

The Singing School

Words and Music by P. Benson   *1869*

Gently satirized in this nonsense song, the singing school was a long-established part of American musical tradition.

Laura loved the singing school and its gay evenings. First the class learned the notes; then they practiced scales, exercises, and songs. At recess everyone talked and laughed together. And on the way home with Almanzo, Laura sang this song again.   HGY, *page 212*

1. Oh, child-hood's joys are ver - y great, A - swing-in' on his moth - er's gate, A - eat - in' can - dy till his mouth Is all stuck up from north to south, And oth - er things he

2. And it's con - sid - ered ver - y nice, To skate up - on the friz up ice, Un - less you chance to fall ker - whack! And there - by cause your head to crack. And when you go from

3. Some think that nothing's half so good,
   As oysters roasted, fried, or stewed,
   And others think the pleasure's more
   A-slidin' on a cellar door.
   So some think this and some think that,
   But all agree there's greater sat-
   Isfaction to be always had,
   At singing school as I have said.

   (Chorus)

4. Oh, sweet the breath of dewy morn,
   A-blowin' sadly through the corn,
   While golden rays of mystic light
   Is heard upon the dawn of night.
   But superfine, ecstatic bliss,
   You'll always find and never miss,
   If you will only mind this rule,
   And always go to singing school.

   (Chorus)

Captain Jinks

Words by William Horace Lingard   Music by T. Maclagan   1869

This is an English music-hall number that was an instant success when intro-
duced in the United States. The "horse" referred to is not a four-legged one but
the troop of marines for whose rations their captain was responsible.

Ma set a pan of beautiful, brown baked beans and a pan of golden corn bread
on the table. Then Pa sang: "I'm Captain Jinks...."   BPC, *page 338*

With bouncy humor

1. I'm Cap - tain Jinks of the Horse Ma - rines, I
2. I joined my corps when twen - ty - one, Of

of - ten go be - yond my means, To court the girls all
course I thought it cap - i - tal fun, When the en - e - my came then

in their teens, And cut a swell in the ar - my. I teach the la - dies
off I run, I was-n't cut out for the ar - my. When I left home, ma-

how to dance, How to dance, how to dance, I
ma she cried, Ma - ma she cried, ma - ma she cried, When

teach the la - dies how to dance, For I'm their pet in the ar - my.
I left home, ma - ma she cried, "He ain't cut out for the ar - my."

Chorus

I'm __ Cap - tain Jinks of the Horse Ma - rines, I

64

feed my horse on corn and beans, Al - though 'tis far be -

yond my means, For I'm cap - tain in the ar - my.

3. The first day I went out to drill,
   The bugle sound made me quite ill,
   At the balance step my hat it fell,
   And that wouldn't do for the army.
   The officers they all did shout,
   They all did shout, they all did shout,
   The officers they all did shout,
   "Oh, that's the curse of the army."

   (Chorus)

4. My tailor's bills came in so fast,
   Forced me one day to leave at last,
   And ladies too no more did cast
   Sheep's eyes at me in the army.
   My creditors at me did shout,
   At me did shout, at me did shout,
   My creditors at me did shout,
   "Why, kick him out of the army."

   (Chorus)

Old Dan Tucker

Words and Music by Daniel Decatur Emmett   1843

A robust ballad with many stanzas that has become known as a traditional
American song. The tune is often used for folk dancing.

Mr. Edwards, the family friend, danced to the fiddle's music like a jumping
jack in the moonlight. When it was time to go home, Pa played him down the
road with "Old Dan Tucker." LHP, *page 69*

1. Old Dan Tuck-er was a fine old man, He washed his face in the fry-ing pan, He combed his hair with a wag-on wheel And died of the tooth-ache in his heel.—
2. Old Dan Tuck - er went to town, Rid - ing a mule and lead-ing a houn'; Houn' barked and the mule jumped, Threw old Dan right o-ver a stump.

Chorus

Git out the way for old Dan Tuck-er! He's too late to git his sup-per,

Sup-per's o - ver and dish-es washed, Noth-ing left but a piece of squash!

3. I come to town the other night,
   I hear the noise and saw the fight;
   The watchman was arunnin' roun'
   Crying "Old Dan Tucker's come to town."

   (Chorus)

4. Old Dan he went down to the mill
   To get some meal to put in the swill;
   The miller swore by the point of his knife
   He never see'd such a man in his life.

   (Chorus)

5. Tucker is a nice old man,
   He used to ride our darby ram;
   He sent him whizzin' down the hill,
   If he hadn't got up, he'd lay there still.

   (Chorus)

6. Old Dan begun in early life
   To play the banjo and the fife;
   He play the children all to sleep,
   And then into his bunk he creep.

   (Chorus)

Old Grimes

Words adapted from "Old Grimes" by Albert Gorton Greene

Tune: "Auld Lang Syne" Circa 1873

Pa sang his own version of Greene's song while Ma was making cheese. He thought Old Grimes might have staggered along if his wife hadn't skimmed off every bit of cream. But "She was a mean, tight-fisted woman. Old Grimes got so thin the wind blew him away," Pa said. LHBW, *page 192*

Slow, with mock sadness

Old Grimes is dead, that good old man, We
ne'er shall see him more, He used to wear an
old grey coat, All but-toned down be-fore. Old Grimes's wife made

skim - milk cheese, Old Grimes he drank the whey, There

came an east wind from the west And blew Old Grimes a - way.

Polly-Wolly-Doodle

Words and Music Traditional USA

An exuberant bit of foolery, this song is believed to be of Negro or minstrel origin. It has become a favorite of college glee clubs.

When Pa had agreed that he and Laura could buy an organ for Mary, he said: "By jinks! I feel like celebrating. Bring me my fiddle, Half-Pint, and we'll have a little music." HGY, *page 155*

3. Oh, a grasshopper sittin' on a railroad track,
   Sing polly-wolly-doodle all the day;
   A-pickin' his teeth with a carpet tack,
   Sing polly-wolly-doodle all the day.

   (Chorus)

4. Oh, I went to bed but it wasn't no use,
   Sing polly-wolly-doodle all the day;
   My feet stuck out for a chicken roost,
   Sing polly-wolly-doodle all the day.

   (Chorus)

5. Behind the barn, down on my knees,
   Sing polly-wolly-doodle all the day;
   I thought I heard that chicken sneeze,
   Sing polly-wolly-doodle all the day.

   (Chorus)

6. He sneezed so hard with the whoopin' cough,
   Sing polly-wolly-doodle all the day;
   He sneezed his head and his tail right off,
   Sing polly-wolly-doodle all the day.

   (Chorus)

71

Pop! Goes the Weasel

Words and Music Traditional USA

A standard tune at country dances, this song goes back to Old English sources. Once Pa said to Laura and Mary, "Watch, and maybe you can see the weasel pop out this time." "Pop!" said his finger on the string; "Goes the weasel!" sang the fiddle. But Laura and Mary hadn't seen Pa's finger make the string pop. He was so quick they could never catch him.   LHBW, *page 99*

wea - sel! All a - round the cob - bler's bench, The
mon - key chased the wea - sel, The preach - er kissed the
cob - bler's wife — Pop! goes the wea - sel!

Uncle John *(A Singing Game)*

Words Traditional USA   Tune: "Yankee Doodle"

This singing game is a love story. It may have been derived from the medieval song in which an imprisoned knight is saved from death by the daughter of a king who keeps him in confinement.

At Laura's first school the little girls always played ring-around-a-rosy at recess till one day she said: "Let's play Uncle John!" BPC, *page 158*

1. Uncle John is sick a-bed, What shall we send him? A piece of pie, a piece of cake, A piece of ap-ple dump-ling.

What shall we send it in?
Who shall we send it by?

In a piece of pa - per. Pa - per is not
By the gov - er - nor's daugh - ter. Take her by the

fine e - nough;___ In a gold - en sau - cer.
lil - y-white hand, And lead her o'er the wa - ter.

2. "_____" so they say,
Goes acourting night and day,
Sword and pistol by his side,
And "_____" to be his bride.
Takes her by the lily-white hand,
And leads her o'er the water,
Here's a kiss, and there's a kiss,
For Mr. _____'s daughter.

DIRECTIONS:
1. *The players circle and sing the first verse.*
2. *At the words "governor's daughter" all fall down.*
3. *The last one down stands apart and whispers to a friend the name of a favorite person and then returns to the ring and stands in the center.*
4. *The friend announces the name, and the players circle again, singing the second verse with the names of the couple inserted at the proper places.*
5. *At the end, the ring breaks up. Everyone dances around, clapping his hands.*

Weevily Wheat

Words and Music Traditional USA

There are memories of the Jacobite uprising of 1745 and of Bonnie Prince Charlie in this dance song. It was widely used at play-parties with the steps of the Virginia Reel.

When Pa was safe at home after being snowed in at Plum Creek, he said: "Laura, if you bring me the fiddle box, I'll play you a tune." Then he filled the house with this jaunty music. BPC, *page 336*

1. Oh, Char - ley he's a fine young man, Oh,
2. Char - ley's here and Char - ley's there And

Char - ley he's a dan - dy! Char - ley likes to
Char - ley's o - ver the o - cean, Char - ley he'll come

kiss the girls And he can do it han - dy!
back some day Un - less he takes a no - tion.

3. Coffee grows on white-oak trees,
   River flows with brandy,
   Choose you one to roam with you
   Sweet as 'lasses candy.

   (Chorus)

Patriotic Songs

The Star-Spangled Banner

Words by Francis Scott Key   Music by John Stafford Smith   1814

The words of our national anthem were written during the bombardment of
Fort McHenry, near Baltimore, during the War of 1812. They were set to
"Anacreon in Heaven," an English melody.

At the Fourth of July celebration when Almanzo was a little boy, the band
played and everybody sang: "Oh, say, can you see. . . ."   FB, *page 178*

1. Oh __ say, can you see, by the dawn's ear - ly light, What so
2. On the shore dim - ly seen through the mists of the deep Where the
3. Oh __ thus be it ev - er, when __ free men shall stand Be -

proud - ly we hailed at the twi-light's last gleam - ing? Whose broad stripes and bright
foe's haugh - ty host in dread si - lence re - pos - es, What is that which the
tween their loved home and the war's des - o - la - tion! Bless'd with vic-to - ry and

stars, through the per - il - ous fight, O'er the ram - parts we watched were so
breeze, o'er the tow - er - ing steep As it fit - ful - ly blows, half con-
peace, may the heav-en-res-cued land Praise the Power that hath made and pre-

gal - lant - ly stream - ing. And the rock-et's red glare, the bombs burst-ing in
ceals, half dis - clos - es; Now it catch-es the gleam of the morn-ing's first
served us a na - tion! Then con-quer we must, when our cause it is

air, Gave proof through the night that our flag was still there.
beam, In full glo - ry re - flect - ed now shines on the stream.
just, And this be our mot - to: "In __ God is our trust!"

Chorus

Oh! say, does that __ star - span - gled ban - ner __ yet __
'Tis the star - span - gled __ ban - ner! Oh, long may __ it __
And the star - span - gled __ ban - ner in tri - umph __ shall __

wave __ O'er the land __ of the free and the home of the brave?
wave __ O'er the land __ of the free and the home of the brave!
wave __ O'er the land __ of the free and the home of the brave!

When Johnny Comes Marching Home

Words and Music by Patrick Gilmore   (pseud. Louis Lambert)   1863

Patrick Gilmore, a famous bandmaster, published this song under the pseudo-
nym Louis Lambert. It has been a favorite ever since the Civil War.
The night of Pa's return from working as a harvester, he looked round at Ma
and the girls and said: "I have missed this." Then he began to play songs of
home.   BPC, *page 244*

1. When John - ny comes march - ing home a - gain, Hur - rah,_____ hur -
2. The old church bell will peal with joy, Hur - rah,_____ hur -
3. Get read - y for the jub - i - lee, Hur - rah,_____ hur -

rah,_____ We'll give him a heart - y wel - come then, Hur -
rah,_____ To wel - come home our dar - ling boy, Hur -
rah,_____ We'll give the he - ro three times three, Hur -

Hail Columbia

Words by Joseph Hopkinson   Music by Philip Phile   1798

This song was written at a time when war with France was thought to be inevitable. For many years it rivaled "The Star-Spangled Banner" as one of our great patriotic songs.

After supper the Ingalls family all gathered near the warmth of the stove, and Pa sang: "Hail, ye heroes, Heaven born band!"   SSL, *page 154*

Majestic march tempo

1. Hail! Co-lum-bia, hap-py land! Hail! ye he-roes,
2. Im-mor-tal pa-triots, rise once more! De-fend your rights, de-

heav'n-born band! Who fought and bled in Free-dom's_ cause,
fend your shore! Let no rude foe, with im-pious_ hand,

Who fought and bled in Free-dom's_ cause, And when the storm of
Let no rude foe, with im-pious_ hand, In-vade the shrine where

Chorus

Firm, u-ni-ted, let us be, Ral-ly-ing round our lib-er-ty;

As a band of broth-ers join'd, Peace and safe-ty we shall find.

3. Sound, sound the trump of fame!
   Let Washington's great name
   Ring through the world with loud applause!
   Ring through the world with loud applause!
   Let ev'ry clime to freedom dear,
   Listen with a joyful ear!
   With equal skill, with godlike power,
   He governs in the fearful hour
   Of horrid war, or guides with ease
   The happier times of honest peace.

   (Chorus)

4. Behold the chief who now commands!
   Once more to serve his country stands!
   The rock on which the storm will beat,
   The rock on which the storm will beat,
   But arm'd in virtue firm and true,
   His hopes are fix'd on Heaven and you;
   When hope was sinking in dismay,
   When glooms obscured Columbia's day;
   His steady mind, from changes free,
   Resolved on death or liberty!

   (Chorus)

Uncle Sam's Farm

Words and Music by Jesse Hutchinson, Jr.
Original music arranged by N. Barker   1850

Concert tours of singing families were a popular form of musical entertainment in the United States from 1840 to 1860. Best-known were the Hutchinsons. Jesse Hutchinson, Jr., wrote a number of their songs.

Pa sang this song often as he drove westward to the Dakota Territory. Even baby Grace joined in though she didn't bother to follow the tune.   SSL, *page 62*

1. Of ___ all the might - y na - tions In the east or in the west, Oh, this
2. St. ___ Law - rence marks our north - ern line As fast her wa - ters flow; And the

glo - rious Yan - kee na - tion Is the great - est and the best, We have
Ri - o Grande our south - ern bound, 'Way down to Mex - i - co; From the

room for all cre - a - tion And our ban — ner is un-furl'd, Here's a
great At - lan - tic O - cean Where the sun be - gins to dawn, Leap a -

gen - 'ral in - vi - ta - tion To the peo - ple of the world.
cross the Rock - y Moun - tains Far a - way to O - re - gon.

Chorus

Oh, come a - way! Come a - way!

Come a-way, I say! Oh, come a-way! Come a-way! Come right a-way! Oh,—

come to this coun-try and have no fear of harm, Our_ Un-cle Sam is rich e-nough To

give us all a farm!

3. While the South shall raise the cotton
   And the West the corn and pork,
   New England manufactories
   Shall do up the finer work,
   For the deep and flowing waterfalls
   That course along our hills,
   Are just the thing for washing sheep
   And driving cotton mills.

   (Chorus)

4. Our fathers gave us Liberty
   But little did they dream,
   The grand results that pour along
   This mighty age of steam,
   For our mountains, lakes, and rivers
   Are all a blaze of fire,
   And we send our news by lightning
   On the telegraphic wire.

   (Chorus)

5. Yes! we're bound to beat the nations
   For our motto's "Go ahead,"
   And we'll tell the foreign countries
   That our people are well-fed,
   For the nations must remember
   That Uncle Sam is not a fool,
   For the people do the voting
   And the children go to school.

   (Chorus)

America

Words by Reverend Samuel Francis Smith   Traditional English Tune   1831

The words to this song were written at the request of Lowell Mason, the "father of public-school music in the United States." They were first sung at a children's celebration of Independence Day in Boston. When Laura heard them, her whole mind seemed to be lighted up by their message of freedom under Divine Law. LTP, *page 76*

3. Let music swell the breeze,
   And ring from all the trees
   Sweet freedom's song;
   Let mortal tongues awake;
   Let all that breathe partake;
   Let rocks their silence break
   The sound prolong.

4. Our father's God to Thee,
   Author of liberty,
   To Thee we sing;
   Long may our land be bright
   With freedom's holy light;
   Protect us by Thy might,
   Great God, our King!

Love and Courtship

The Blue Juniata

Words and Music by Mrs. Marion Dix Sullivan   1844

Although the Juniata is a little river in Pennsylvania, Ma sang this highly romanticized ballad out on the prairie. When Laura asked her where the voice of Alfarata went, Ma answered, "Oh, I suppose she went West. That's what Indians do." Then Pa explained how the government was moving the Indians westward and how the settlers were taking over their land.   LHP, *page 235*

With motion and strong beat

1. Wild roved an In - dian maid, Bright Al - fa -
2. "Bold is my war - rior good, The love of Al - fa -
3. So sang the In - dian maid, Bright Al - fa -

ra - ta, Where flow the wa - ters Of the
ra - ta, Proud wave his sun - ny plumes A -
ra - ta, Where sweep the wa - ters Of the

Come In and Shut the Door

Words by J. P. H.   Music by J. G. Callcott   1863

One snowy Christmas Eve Laura missed Almanzo, who was visiting his old home far away. He might forget her, she thought, or wish that he had not given her a ring. . . . Someone knocked at the door. When Laura opened it, she could not believe her eyes for there stood Almanzo himself. "Come in!" Pa called. "Come in and shut the door!"   HGY, *page 227*

A little fast, playfully

1. Oh,__ do not stand so long out-side, Why need you be so shy! The__ peo-ple's ears are
2. Nay__ do not say "No, thank you, Jane," With such a bash-ful smile; You__ said when la-dies
3. You__ say I did not an-swer you, To what you said last night; I ___ heard your ques-tion

Green Grows the Laurel

Words and Music Traditional USA

A very old song of lovers' parting and reunion. The words "orange and blue" refer to William of Orange. In the United States they were sometimes changed to "red, white, and blue." Out on the prairie Pa sang this to Ma when he was leaving for an overnight trip to town. LHP, *page 207*

1. I once had a sweet-heart, but now I've got none, She's gone and she's left me to weep and to moan; She's gone and she's left me, but con-tent-ed I'll be, For I'll get an-oth-er one bet-ter than she.

2. She wrote me a let-ter, four red ros-y lines, She wrote me an-oth-er all twist-ed in twines;___ Keep your love let-ter and I will keep mine, And write to your sweet-heart and I'll write to mine.

So green grows the laurel, and so does the rue, So woe-ful, my love, at the part-ing with you. But by our next meet-ing our love we'll re-new; We'll change the green lau-rel to the or-ange and blue.

3. She passes my window both early and late,
   And the looks that she gives me, they make my heart break,
   And the looks that she gives me a thousand times o'er,
   "You are the sweetheart I once did adore."

   (Chorus)

4. I ofttimes do wonder why young maids love men,
   I ofttimes do wonder why young men love them;
   But by my experience, I now ought to know
   Young maids are deceivers wherever they go.

   (Chorus)

In Dreamland Far Away

Words by George Birdseye   Music by Hart Pease Danks   1887

George Birdseye was a New York journalist and a friend of Stephen Foster.
Hart Pease Danks is the composer of "Silver Threads Among the Gold."
Lamplight shone from the windows of the little prairie house. Pa was playing
the fiddle; his voice rose with the music of this song, one that he often sang to
Ma.   HGY, *page 216*

1. A beau-ti-ful cas-tle I've built for thee, In
2. No sor-row shall en-ter our cas-tle walls, For

dream-land far a-way, _____ And there, gen-tle dar-ling, come
joy shall guard the door; _____ No word shall be spo-ken that

Chorus

dwell with me, Where love — a - lone — has sway. ___
e'er re-calls The cares _ we knew _ be - fore. ___ Oh, sweet will be our

bliss - es, Oh, rare _ will be ___ our bliss - es! We'll

tell ___ our time by the lov - ers' chime, That strikes _ the hour _ with kiss - es.

3. Then let us enjoy ev'ry blissful hour!
   Too soon our dreams will break;
   Alas, that we never may have the pow'r
   To live them when we wake!

   (Chorus)

In the Starlight

Words by J. E. Carpenter   Music by Stephen Glover   1843

J. E. Carpenter and Stephen Glover wrote a number of songs together. This charming piece has been included in many collections.

As Almanzo and Laura were driving back from singing school, he said: "I don't know when I ever saw the stars so bright." Softly, Laura began to sing the starlight song.   HGY, *page 207*

A little fast

1. In the star-light, in the star-light, Let us wan-der__ gay__ and__
2. In the star-light, in the star-light, At the day-light's dew-y__

free,   For there's noth-ing in the day-light Half so
close,   When the night-in-gale is sing-ing His last

Whip-Poor-Will's Song

Words and Music by Harrison Millard   1865

Pa said, "I want to try a song I heard a fellow singing the other day. He whistled the chorus. I believe the fiddle will beat his whistling." Pa sang low and longingly, and "Whip-poor-will" the fiddle answered, fluting and throbbing like the throat of the bird.   LTP, *page 136*

1. Oh, meet me when day-light is fad - ing, And is dark - en - ing in - to the night, When song-birds are sing-ing their ves - pers, And the

2. 'Tis said that what-ev-er sweet feel - ings May be throb-bing with-in a fond heart, When list-'ning to whip-poor-will's sing - ing, For a

day has far van-ished from sight;
twelve-month will nev - er de - part;

And then I will tell to you,
So then we will meet in the

dar - ling,
wood -land,

All the love I have cher-ished so long,
Far a - way from the hur-ry-ing throng,

If
And

you will but meet me at eve - ning,
whis-per our love to each oth - er,

When you
When we

hear the first whip-poor-will's
hear the first whip-poor-will's

3. And in the long years of the future,
   Though our duties may part us awhile,
   And on the return of this evening,
   We'll be severed by many a mile;
   Yet deep in our bosoms we'll cherish
   The affection, so fervent and strong,
   We pledged to each other this evening,
   When we heard the first whip-poor-will's song.

   (Chorus)

Oh, Whistle and I'll Come to You, My Lad!

Words by Robert Burns   Traditional Scottish Tune   1799

Like most of Burns' songs, the words of this song are partly traditional, partly
his own, and are set to a folk melody.

When Laura sang: "Oh, whistle and I'll come to you, my lad," Almanzo
asked: "Would you?" "Of course not!" she answered. "That's only a song."
HGY, *page 184*

Oh,— whis - tle and I'll — come to you, my lad, Oh,—
whis - tle and I'll — come to you, my lad, Though fa - ther and mith - er and
a' should gae mad, Oh,— whis - tle and I'll — come to you, my lad.

Verse

1. But __ war - i - ly tent when ye come to court me, __ And __
2. At __ kirk, or at mar - ket, where - 'er you meet me, __ Gang __
3. Aye, __ vow and pro - test that you care na for me, __ And __

come na un - less the back - yett be a - jee; Syne __
by me as tho' that you car'd not a flie; But __
whyles you may light - ly my beau - ty a wee; But __

up the back - style, and let nae - bod - y see, And __ come __ as you were na
steal me a blink o' your bon - nie black e'e, Yet __ look __ as you were na
court na an - ith - er, tho' jok - in' you be, For __ fear that she wyle __ your

D.C. al Fine

com - ing to me, And __ come __ as you were na com - ing to me.
look - ing at me, Yet __ look __ as you were na look - ing at me.
fan - cy frae me, For __ fear that she wyle __ your fan - cy frae me.

Wait for the Wagon

Words and Music Anonymous, USA   Circa 1851

An old favorite that is still heard today, "Wait for the Wagon" has often been paraphrased and used as a campaign song. When Pa began to sing it as the family rode to church, Ma said "Charles" softly to remind him that it was Sunday. Then all together they sang: "There is a happy land...."   BPC, *page 181*

1. Will you come with me, my Phil - lis dear, To yon blue moun - tain free, Where the blos - soms smell the sweet - est, Come

2. (Oh,) ev - 'ry Sun - day morn - ing My wife is at my side, A - wait - ing for the wag - on, And

rove a-long with me.　2. Oh,　we'll all take a　ride!

Chorus

Wait for the wag-on,　Wait for the wag-on,

Wait for the wag-on, And we'll all take a ride.

D. C.　*last time only*

3. Your lips are red as poppies,
   Your hair so slick and neat,
   All braided up with dahlias,
   And hollyhocks so sweet.

4. It's ev'ry Sunday morning,
   When I am by your side,
   We'll jump into the wagon,
   And all take a ride.

   (Chorus)

5. Together on life's journey,
   We'll travel till we stop,
   And if we have no trouble,
   We'll reach the happy top.

6. Then come with me, sweet Phillis,
   My dear, my lovely bride,
   We'll jump into the wagon,
   And all take a ride.

   (Chorus)

Beware!

Words by Henry Wadsworth Longfellow   Music by Charles Moulton 1865

The original of Longfellow's poem warns against a flirtatious maiden. But when Cousin Lena sang "Beware!" at Silver Lake, it was about a young man who would prove untrue. As Laura and Lena climbed into the buggy, the black ponies gave a little squeal and ran. Everything went rushing by too fast to be seen. Lena began to sing, and Laura joined in with all her voice.   SSL, *page 48*

Chorus

A | A#dim | Bm | | E

Trust her not, she's fool - ing thee; She's

E7 | A | | | A#dim

fool - ing thee; _____ Trust her

Bm | | A | E7 | A

not, she's fool - ing thee;_ She's fool - ing thee._____

3. And she has hair of golden hue,
   Take care! take care!
   And what she says, it is not true,
   Beware! beware!

   (Chorus)

4. She gives thee a garland woven fair,
   Take care! take care!
   It is a fool's cap for thee to wear,
   Beware! beware!

   (Chorus)

The Girl I Left Behind Me

Words Traditional USA   Traditional Irish Tune

This tune was first printed in Dublin in 1810. It is the traditional type of music played by a band when troops are leaving. This Western version is also used for square dancing. Pa sang it to Ma when he came back from his long trip to the wheatfields where he had been working as a harvester. BPC, *page 244*

1. I struck the trail in sev-en-ty-two, The herd strung out be-
2. The wind did blow, the rain did flow, The hail did fall and

hind me; As I jogged a-long, my mind ran back To the
blind me; I thought of the girl, the sweet lit-tle girl, The

girl I left be-hind me. The sweet lit-tle girl, the
girl I'd left be-hind me! The sweet lit-tle girl, the

pret - ty lit - tle girl, The girl I left be - hind me, As I
pret - ty lit - tle girl, The girl I left be - hind me, I ___

jogged a - long, my mind ran back To the girl I left be - hind me!
thought of the girl, the sweet lit-tle girl, The girl I'd left be - hind me!

3. She wrote ahead to the place I said
   A letter to remind me;
   She says, "I am true; when you get through
   Ride back and you will find me."
   The sweet little girl, the pretty little girl,
   The girl I left behind me,
   She says, "I am true; when you get through
   Ride back and you will find me."

4. If ever I get off the trail,
   And the Indians they don't find me,
   I'll make my way straight back again
   To the girl I left behind me.
   The sweet little girl, the pretty little girl,
   The girl I left behind me,
   I'll make my way straight back again
   To the girl I left behind me!

The Big Sunflower

Words and Music by Bobby Newcomb 1868

The theme song of Billy Emerson, the well-known minstrel, this cheerful tune was Pa's "trouble song." He sang it when blizzards turned the windows into a white blur and snow blew through every crack until it had to be shoveled off the beds in the morning.   SSL, *page 250*

1. There is a charm I can't ex-plain, A-bout a girl I've
2. As days passed on and we be-came Like friends of old-en
3. I went next day dressed in my best This young girl for to

seen, My__ heart beats fast when she goes past In a
times, I__ thought the ques-tion I would pop And__
see, To__ ask her if she would ex-plain Why__

dark dress trimmed in green. Her eyes are bright as
ask her to be mine. But the an - swer I re -
she had shak - en me. She said she real - ly

eve - ning stars, So lov - ing and so shy, And the
ceived next day, How could she treat me so? In -
felt quite sad To cause me such dis - tress; And

folks all stop and look a - round When - ev - er she goes by.
stead of be - ing mine for life She sim - ply an - swered "No."
when I said "Won't you be mine?" Of course she an - swered "Yes."

Chorus

Oh, I am as hap - py as a big sun - flower That

nods and bends in the breez - es, And my heart is as light as the

wind that blows The__ leaves from off the trees - es.

The Gum-Tree Canoe

Words by S. S. Steele   Music by A. F. Winnemore   1847

An old-time minstrel standby, this song is also called "Tombigbee River."
When it was time for Laura to go to sleep in the covered wagon, the voice of
the fiddle began a long swinging rhythm. As her eyelids closed she seemed to
drift over endless seas of prairie grasses to the sound of "Row away, row o'er
the waters so blue." LHP, *page 335*

With a lilt

1. On —— Tom - big - bee Riv - er so bright I was
2. All the day in the field the soft cot - ton I

born, In a hut made of husks of the tall yel - low corn, And ——
hoe, I —— think of my Ju - lia and sing as I go, Oh, I

there I first met with my Ju - lia so true, And I
catch her a bird with a wing of true blue, And at

3. With my hands on the banjo and toe on the oar,
   I sing to the sound of the river's soft roar,
   While the stars they look down at my Julia so true
   And dance in her eye in our gum-tree canoe.

   (Chorus)

4. One night the stream bore us so far away
   That we couldn't come back so we thought we'd just stay,
   Oh, we spied a tall ship with a flag of true blue,
   And it took us in tow with our gum-tree canoe.

   (Chorus)

A Railroad Man for Me

Words and Music Traditional USA

A "courting song," many examples of which are found in American folklore.
At Silver Lake, Laura and Lena met every morning and every evening to take
care of the cows. They led them to drink and moved the picket pins to fresh
grass; then they did the milking and sang. Sometimes they sang softly about
marrying a railroad man.   SSL, *page 93*

1. I wouldn't marry a farmer, He's always in the dirt, I'd rather marry a
2. I wouldn't marry a blacksmith, He's always in the black, I'd rather marry an

rail - road man Who wears a strip - ed shirt!
en - gi - neer That throws the throt - tle back.

Chorus

Oh, a rail - road man,__ a rail - road man, A

rail - road man for me! I'm going to mar - ry a

rail - road man, A rail-road-er's bride__ I'll be!__

My Heart Is Sair

Barbary Allen

Words and Music Traditional English

This old ballad was brought to this country by the early colonists. There are many variants of the words and music, but the story remains essentially the same. Moonlight shone through the southern window and touched Pa's face and hands and the fiddle as the bow moved smoothly over the strings while he sang. SSL, *page 290*

Simply, ballad style

1. In Scar - let Town where I was born, There
2. All in the mer - ry month of May, When

was a fair maid dwell - in', __ And ev - 'ry youth cried __
green buds they were swell - in', __ Young John - nie Grove on his

"Well - a - wa'!" Her name was Bar - bary Al - len. __
death - bed lay For love of Bar - bary Al - len. __

3. He sent his man un-to her then, To the
4.(So) slow-ly, slow - ly, she came up, And

town where she did dwell in, — Say-ing "You must come to my
slow-ly she came nigh him; — And all she said when

mas - ter If your name be Bar - bary Al - len."
there she came, "Young man, I think you're dy - ing." 4. So

5. He turned his face unto the wall,
    And death was with him dealin',
    "Adieu, adieu, to all my friends,
    Adieu to Barbary Allen."

6. As she was walking o'er the fields,
    She heard the bells aknellin',
    And every stroke did seem to say
    "Unworthy Barbary Allen."

7. When he was dead and laid in grave,
    Her heart was struck with sorrow,
    "O Mother, Mother, make my bed,
    For I shall die tomorrow."

8. She on her deathbed as she lay
    Begged to be buried by him,
    And sore repented of the day
    That she did e'er deny him.

9. "Farewell," she said, "ye virgins all,
    And shun the fault I fell in,
    Henceforth take warning by the fall
    Of cruel Barbary Allen."

Bonny Doon

Words by Robert Burns *Traditional Scottish Tune* *1792*

In a letter written in 1794, Burns says this tune "was composed a good many years ago by an amateur playing on the black keys of the harpsichord."
When everyone sang together in the surveyors' house at Silver Lake, Laura had never been so happy, and she was happiest of all when they were singing this plaintive air. SSL, *page 213*

Ye'll break my heart, ye little birds, That
Wi' lightsome heart I pu'd a rose, Full

wanton through the flow'ring thorn, Ye mind me of departed joys, Departed never to return.
sweet upon its thorny tree; But my false lover stole the rose, And left the thorn behind wi' me.

Highland Mary

Words by Robert Burns   Traditional Scottish Tune   1799

Burns wrote to his friend George Thomson about the poem on which this song is based: "It pleases myself; I think it is in my happiest manner." It appeared in Thomson's *Scottish Airs*, set to the tune of "Katherine Ogle." This was Mary's favorite song. "It's sweet," she said. "It's sweet but it's sad," said Laura. ssl, *page 154*

Somewhat slowly

1. Ye __ banks and braes and streams a - round The __ cas - tle o' __ Mont - gom - er - y, Green __ be your __ woods and fair your flowers, Your __ wa - ters __ nev - er __ drum - lie! There __
2. How __ sweet - ly bloomed the gay green birk, How __ rich the haw - thorn's blos - som, As __ un - der - neath their fra - grant shade, I __ clasped her __ to __ my __ bos - om! The __

sum - mer ___ first un - falds ___ her ___ robes, And ___
gold - en ___ hours on an - gel ___ wings Flew ___

there the ___ lang - est ___ tar - ry; For ___ there I took the
o'er me ___ and ___ my dear - ie; For ___ dear to me as

last ___ fare - weel O' ___ my ___ sweet High - land ___ Ma - ry.
light ___ and ___ life, Was ___ my ___ sweet High - land ___ Ma - ry.

3. Wi' mony a vow and lock'd embrace,
   Our parting was fu' tender,
   And, pledging aft to meet again,
   We tore oursels asunder;
   But, oh, fell death's untimely frost,
   That nipped my flower sae early!
   Now green's the sod and cauld's the clay
   That wraps my Highland Mary!

4. Oh, pale, pale now those rosy lips
   I oft ha'e kiss'd sae fondly!
   And closed for aye the sparkling glance,
   That dwelt on me sae kindly!
   And mouldering now in silent dust,
   That heart that lo'ed me dearly;
   But still within my bosom's core
   Shall live my Highland Mary.

Lily Dale

Words and Music by H. S. Thompson   1852

This song is a favorite lament for a departed maiden. The melody became the
theme for a schottische with variations, as well as for an ornate piano version.
It was Christmas Eve in the sod house beside Plum Creek. Pa tuned the fiddle,
rosined the bow, and sang about sweet Lily Dale.   BPC, *page 336*

1. 'Twas a calm, still night, And the moon's pale light Shone soft o'er hill and vale, When friends mute with grief Stood around the death-bed Of my poor lost Lil-y Dale.
2. "I go," she said, "To the land of rest, And ere my strength shall fail, I must tell you where Near my own loved home, You must lay poor Lil-y Dale."

Chorus

Oh! Lil - y, sweet Lil - y, dear Lil - y Dale, Now the wild rose blos - soms O'er her lit-tle green grave, 'Neath the trees in the flow - 'ry vale.

3. "'Neath the chestnut tree,
Where the wild flowers grow,
And the stream ripples forth through the vale,
Where the birds shall warble
Their songs in the spring
There lay poor Lily Dale."

(Chorus)

My Heart Is Sair for Somebody

Words by Robert Burns   Traditional Scottish Tune   1796

There may be echoes of Jacobite sentiment in this song, for James Stuart, the Old Pretender, was spoken of as "Somebody."

The house on the prairie was full of Christmas plans and secrets; there were popcorn balls and little bags of candy in pink mosquito netting. Then Pa said, "Let's have a little music before we begin on these good things."   HGY, *page 226*

Slowly, with expression

1. My heart is sair, I dare - na tell, My
2. Ye pow'rs that smile on vir - tuous love, O,

heart is sair for some - bod - y. O, I could wake a
sweet - ly smile on some - bod - y. Frae il - ka dan - ger

win - ter night, A' for the sake o' some - bod - y!
keep him free, And send me safe my some - bod - y.

Chorus

O - hone! for some - bod - y!

O - hey! for some - bod - y! I could range the
I would do, what

world a - round For the sake o' some - bod - y.
would I not, For the sake o' some - bod - y?

Kitty Wells

Words by Thomas Sloan, Jr.   Music by Charles E. Atherton   Circa 1850

Often called "Katy Wells," this song was handed down from memory in numerous versions. It was widely sung in rural areas of the United States.

Laura and Mary were tucked in the trundle bed. Ma's hands were busy sewing by the lamplight. Pa was greasing his boots. He whistled cheerfully as he worked, and then he sang this ballad.   LHBW, *page 116*

Moderately slow, with sentiment

1. You ask what caus - es__ me to weep, Why he like oth-ers is not gay, What makes the tear flow
2. I nev - er shall for - get the day That we to-geth- er roamed the dells; I kissed her cheek and

down his cheek From ear - ly morn 'til close of day. My
named the day That I should mar - ry Kit - ty Wells. But

sto - ry, dear friends, you shall hear, For in my
death came in my cab - in door And took from

mem - 'ry fresh it dwells, 'Twill cause you all to
me my joy, my bride, And when I found she

drop a tear On the grave of my sweet Kit - ty Wells.
was no more, Then I laid my ban - jo down and cried.

3. I often wish that I was dead
   And laid beside her in the tomb;
   The sorrow that bows down my head
   Is silent in the midnight gloom.
   The springtime has no charms for me
   Though flowers are blooming in the dells,
   For that bright form I do not see,
   'Tis the form of my sweet Kitty Wells.

   (Chorus)

Hymns and Sacred Songs

We're All Here: The Song of the Freed Men

Words and Music Traditional USA   1880

Pa's fingers were too stiff from being out in the cold for him to play the fiddle. In hard times before, he had made music for them; now there was none for him. Suddenly Laura remembered the chorus of "The Song of the Freed Men." "We're all here!" she exclaimed. "We can sing!" And she began to hum the tune.   LW, *page 290*

136

We're all here, we're all here, Do thy-self-a no harm; We're

all here, we're all here, Do thy-self-a no harm.

3. As I go down the steps of time,
   Do thyselfa no harm,
   I leave this sinful world behind,
   Do thyselfa no harm.

   (Chorus)

4. If you get there before I do,
   Do thyselfa no harm,
   Tell them I am acoming too,
   Do thyselfa no harm.

   (Chorus)

Am I a Soldier of the Cross?

Words by Isaac Watts   Music by Reverend John Chetham   1724

Isaac Watts, an English Congregationalist pastor, wrote more than six hundred hymns. Many are still used today.

On Sundays Laura and Mary could not run or shout or be noisy in their play. They had to sit quietly and hold their dolls or look at pictures. At bedtime Pa would play and sing "Shall I be carried to the skies...."   LHBW, *page 97*

1. Am I a sol - dier of the Cross, A
2. Shall I be car - ried to the skies On

fol - low'r of the Lamb? And shall I fear to
flow - 'ry beds of ease While oth - ers fought to

own His cause Or blush to speak His name?
win the cause prize And sailed through blood - y seas?

When I Can Read My Title Clear

Words by Isaac Watts   Music by J. P. Holbrook   1709

In addition to hymns and sermons, Isaac Watts was also the author of *Divine and Moral Songs for Children*, a celebrated book of juvenile verse.

On the first night of the four-day blizzard on the prairie, the storm raged outside, hammering at the walls and windows. But the family, safely sheltered and huddled in the warmth of a hay fire, went on singing.   LW, *page 291*

1. When I can read my ti - tle clear
   To man - sions in the skies,
   I'll bid fare - well to ev - 'ry fear
   And wipe my weep - ing eyes.

2. Should earth a - gainst my soul en - gage,
   And hell - ish darts be hurled,
   Then I can smile at Sa - tan's rage
   And face a frown - ing world.

3. Let cares like a wild deluge come,
   And storms of sorrow fall;
   May I but safely reach my home,
   My God, my heaven, my all.

4. There shall I bathe my weary soul
   In seas of heavenly rest,
   And not a wave of trouble roll
   Across my peaceful breast.

The Home of the Soul

Words by Mrs. E. H. Gates   Music by Philip Phillips   1866

At the composer's request, the words to this song were written in the spirit of
The Pilgrim's Progress, the famous allegory by John Bunyan.
The hymn blended with the wailing of the winds outside as Ma sat in her rock-
ing chair and softly sang about the beautiful land "where no storms ever beat."
LW, *page 241*

1. I will sing you a song of that beau-ti-ful land, The far-a-way home of the soul, Where no storms ev-er beat on the glit-ter-ing

2. Oh, the home of the soul! In my vi-sions and dreams, Its bright jas-per walls I can see; Till I fan-cy but dim-ly the veil in-ter-

3. Oh, how sweet it will be in that beau-ti-ful land, So free from all sor-row and pain; With __ songs on our lips and with harps in our

141

Merry, Merry Christmas! *(A Christmas Carol)*

Words and Music by Mrs. T. J. Cook 1871

This carol has a hymnlike quality that makes it suitable for a church Christmas celebration like the wonderful one in Minnesota, where Laura saw her first Christmas tree and realized that everything on the tree was a present for someone! BPC, *page 253*; SSL, *page 187*

Somewhat lively

Chorus

Mer - ry, mer - ry Christ - mas ev - 'ry - where! Cheer-i - ly it ring - eth through the air; Christ - mas bells, Christ - mas trees, Christ -mas o - dors on the breeze. Mer - ry, mer - ry Christ - mas ev - 'ry - where! Cheer - i - ly it ring - eth through the air.

Verse

| D | G | C | D7 |

1. Why should we so joy - ful - ly Sing with grate - ful mirth?
2. Light for wea - ry wan - der-ers, Com - fort for th' op-pressed!
3. Deeds of Faith and Char - i - ty, These our off -'rings be,

| G | C | G | D7 | G |

See, the Sun of Right - eous-ness Beams up - on the earth!
He will guide His trust - ing ones In - to per - fect rest.
Lead - ing ev - 'ry soul to sing Christ was born for me!

My Sabbath Home

Words by Dr. Christopher Ruby Blackall   Music by W. H. Doane   1871

The author, an army surgeon during the Civil War, wrote several Sunday-school songs in collaboration with W. H. Doane, who composed many hymns of the gospel type.

Laura sang this at home when she was a little girl and later in a real Sunday-school class.   HGY, *page 41;* BPC, *page 298*

1. Sweet Sab - bath school more dear to me Than fair - est pal - ace dome, My heart e'er turns with joy to thee, My own dear Sab - bath Home.

2. Here first my will - ful, wan - d'ring heart The way of life was shown; Here first I sought with the bet - ter part And gained a Sab - bath Home.

Chorus

Sab - bath Home! (Sweet Home!) Bless - ed Home! (Sweet Home!) Sab - bath

Home! (Sweet Home!) Bless-ed Home! (Sweet Home!) My heart e'er turns with

joy __ to __ thee, My own dear Sab - bath Home.

3. Here Jesus stands with loving voice,
Entreating me to come
And make of Him my earnest choice,
In this dear Sabbath Home.

(Chorus)

The Ninety and Nine

Words by Elizabeth D. Clephane   Music by Ira D. Sankey   1876

First published in an English magazine, this poem was little-known until Ira D. Sankey came upon it and set it to music. It became the most famous of his gospel songs.

In town everyone went to the revival meetings. There were hymns and prayers and preaching. Laura loved this hymn, but Reverend Brown's thunderous calls for repentance sent chills up her spine.   LTP, *page 276*

1. There were nine - ty and nine that safe - ly lay In the
2. "Lord, Thou hast here Thy nine - ty and nine, Are they

shel - ter of the fold, But one was out on the
not e - nough for Thee?" But the Shep - herd made an - swer:

hills a - way, Far off from the gates of gold. A -
"This of Mine Has wan - dered a - way from Me, And

way   on the moun-tains   wild   and bare,   A - way   from the ten - der
al - though the road   be   rough   and steep,   I   go   to the des - ert   to

D   (G   D)   G   C   G   D7   G

Shep - herd's care,   A - way   from the ten - der   Shep - herd's care.
find __ My   sheep,   I   go   to the des - ert   to   find __ My   sheep."

3.   But none of the ransomed ever knew
       How deep were the waters crossed,
       Nor how dark was the night that the Lord passed through
       Ere He found His sheep that was lost.
       Out in the desert He heard its cry,
       Sick and helpless and ready to die,
       Sick and helpless and ready to die.

4.   "Lord, whence are those blood drops all the way
       That mark out the mountain's track?"
       "They were shed for one who had gone astray
       Ere the Shepherd could bring him back."
       "Lord, whence are Thy hands so rent and torn?"
       "They are pierced tonight by many a thorn,
       They are pierced tonight by many a thorn."

5.   And all through the mountains, thunder-riven,
       And up from the rocky steep
       There rose a cry to the gate of Heaven,
       "Rejoice! I have found My sheep!"
       And the angels echoed around the throne,
       "Rejoice, for the Lord brings back His own!
       Rejoice, for the Lord brings back His own!"

The Old Chariot

Words and Music Traditional USA

A Salvation Army favorite of long ago, this song was based on a Negro spiritual. During the long winter, Pa and some of the men in town set out in a railroad handcar to clear the tracks for the snowbound train. Everyone joined in singing this as they pushed the handlebars up and down. LW, *page 107*

With movement and a strong beat

Chorus

We'll roll the old char - iot a - long, We'll roll the old char - iot a - long, We'll roll the old char - iot a - long, And we won't drag on be - hind!

1. If the sin - ner's in the way, we will
2. If the Dev - il's in the way, we will

stop and take him in, — If the sin-ner's in the way, we will
roll it o - ver him, — If the Dev-il's in the way, we will

stop and take him in, — If the sin-ner's in the way, we will
roll it o - ver him, — If the Dev-il's in the way, we will

D. C. al Fine

stop and take him in, — And we won't drag on be - hind!
roll it o - ver him, — And we won't drag on be - hind!

Sweet By and By

Words by S. Fillmore Bennett   Music by J. P. Webster   1867

This "Christian ballad," written for a collection of Sunday-school hymns, was adopted by Ira D. Sankey for use as a revival number.

After Sunday dinner, Pa played hymn tunes on his fiddle. They sang all afternoon while icy snow beat down upon the house.   LW, *page 130*

1. There's a land that is fair - er than day, And by faith we can see it a - far, For the Fa - ther waits o - ver the way To pre - pare us a dwell - ing place there.

2. We shall sing on that beau - ti - ful shore The me - lo - di - ous songs of the blest, And our spir - its shall sor - row no more, Not a sigh for the bless - ing of rest.

3. To our bountiful Father above,
   We will offer the tribute of praise
   For the glorious gift of His love
   And the blessings that hallow our days.

   (Chorus)

Pull for the Shore

Words and Music by Philip Paul Bliss   Circa 1873

The first words of this famous gospel song always made Laura want to laugh. She remembered how solemnly it had been sung by the tall thin man and the pudgy little one as they made their inebriated way from one to the other of De Smet's two saloons.   LTP, *pages 52, 278*

Moderately

1. Light   in   the dark-ness, sail-or,   day   is   at hand!
2. Trust   in   the life-boat, sail-or,   all   else   will fail;

See   o'er   the foam-ing bil-lows   fair   heav-en's land.
Strong-er   the sur-ges dash, and   fier-cer   the gale;

Drear was the voy-age, sail-or, now al-most o'er;
Heed not the storm-y winds, though loud-ly they roar;

Safe with-in the life-boat, sail-or, pull for the shore.
Watch the bright and morn-ing star, and pull for the shore.

Chorus

Pull for the shore, sail-or, pull for the shore!

Heed not the roll-ing waves, but bend to the oar;

Safe in the life-boat, sail - or, cling to self no more;

Leave the poor old strand - ed wreck, and pull for the shore.

3. Bright gleams the morning, sailor; uplift the eye!
Clouds and darkness disappearing; glory is nigh!
Safe in the lifeboat, sailor, sing evermore,
Glory, glory, hallelujah! Pull for the shore!

(Chorus)

154

There Is a Happy Land

Words and Music by Reverend Andrew Young   1838

Andrew Young, a Scottish schoolmaster, wrote this beloved hymn for children.
When Ma sang it, Laura didn't know she had fallen asleep. She thought shining
angels had begun to sing with Ma and that she was listening to their heavenly
voices.   LHP, *page 220*

1. There is a hap-py land, Far, far a-way, Where saints in glo-ry stand, Bright, bright as day. Oh, to hear the an-gels sing Glo-ry to the Lord, our King.

Loud let His prais - es ring, Praise, praise for aye.

2. Come to that happy land,
   Come, come away;
   Why will ye doubting stand,
   Why still delay?
   Oh, we shall happy be
   When from sin and sorrow free,
   Lord, we shall live with Thee,
   Blest, blest for aye.

3. Bright, in that happy land,
   Beams every eye;
   Kept by a Father's hand,
   Love cannot die.
   Oh, then to glory run;
   Be a crown and kingdom won,
   And bright above the sun,
   We reign for aye.

Index

Song titles are listed in capital letters, first lines of songs in upper-and-lower-case roman.

First lines as they appear in the "Little House" books are in upper-and-lower-case italic.